BOOKS BY
GENE STRATTON-PORTER

The Song of the Cardinal
Freckles
What I Have Done With Birds
At the Foot of the Rainbow
A Girl of the Limberlost
Birds of the Bible

Nellie Hannon,
11 Elmendorf St,
Kingston, N.Y.

1912.

A GIRL OF THE LIMBERLO

"Elnora knelt and slipping her fingers through the leaves
and grasses to the roots, gathered a few violets
and gave them to Philip"

A Girl
of
The Limberlost

By

Gene Stratton-Porter

Illustrations by

Wladyslaw T. Benda

New York
GROSSET & DUNLAP
Publishers

TO
ALL GIRLS OF THE LIMBERLOST
IN GENERAL
AND ONE
JEANNETTE HELEN PORTER
IN PARTICULAR

CONTENTS